Guts

Raina Telgemeier

with color by Braden Lamb

An Imprint of
SCHOLASTIC

This graphic novel is based on personal experiences, though certain
characters, places, and incidents have been modified in service
of the story.

Library of Congress Cataloging-in-Publication Data

Names: Telgemeier, Raina, author, illustrator.
Title: Guts / Raina Telgemeier ; with color by Braden Lamb.
Description: First edition. | New York, NY : Graphix logo, an imprint of Scholastic, 2019.
Identifiers: LCCN 2018050676 (print) | LCCN 2018060290 (ebook)
ISBN 978-0-545-85253-1 (ebook)
ISBN 978-0-545-85251-7 (hardcover : alk. paper)
ISBN 978-0-545-85250-0 (pbk. : alk. paper)
Subjects: LCSH: Stress in children. | Children–Physiology. | Stomach–Diseases.
Classification: LCC BF723.S75 (ebook) | LCC BF723.S75 T45 2019 (print) | DDC 155.4/189042–dc23
LC record available at https://lccn.loc.gov/2018050676

10 9 8 7 6 5 4 3 2 1   19 20 21 22 23
Printed in China   62
First edition, September 2019
Edited by Cassandra Pelham Fulton
Lettering by Jesse Post
Book design by Phil Falco
Author photo by Joseph Fanvu
Publisher: David Saylor

Guts

For anyone who feels afraid

2

4

7

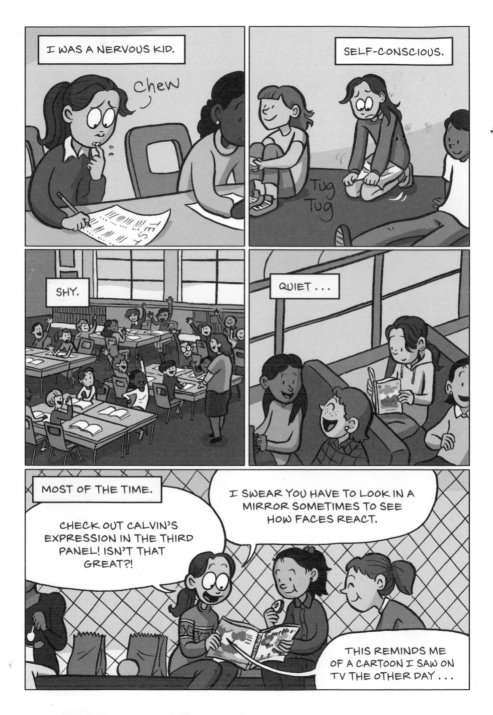

MOM? CAN YOU COME UP HERE?

WHAT IS IT, RAINA? YOU OKAY?

...

IS RAINA SICK, MOM?

YES. SHE NEEDS TO REST.

"SICK" ISN'T QUITE THE RIGHT WORD FOR IT.

BUT SOMETHING WAS DEFINITELY WRONG.

FIFTH GRADE (AND KINDERGARTEN FOR MY SISTER!) STARTED IN SEPTEMBER.

Itchy!

Dorky!

Fancy!

JANE AND NICOLE WERE IN MY CLASS AGAIN!

ROOM 2

MICHELLE, TOO.

MY TEACHER WAS MR. ABRAMS -- WHO I'D ACTUALLY HAD FOR SECOND GRADE, TOO.

HI, RAINA! GREAT TO SEE YOU AGAIN!

YEAH!

THE GIRL SCOUTS OF AMERICA WAS FOUNDED IN 1912 BY JULIETTE GORDON LOW IN SAVANNAH, GEORGIA.

THIS IS WHAT THE GIRL SCOUT LOGO LOOKS LIKE!

44

47

50

ONE TIME AROUND THE COURTYARD... TWO TIMES AROUND THE COURTYARD...

THREE... FOUR...

69

71

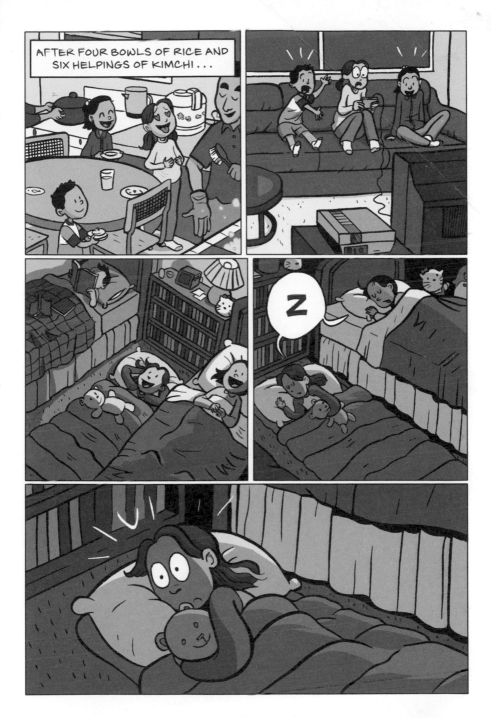

119

THE NEXT DAY

BIG GAME TODAY!! EVERYONE EXCITED?

I'M GOING UPSTAIRS.

AWW, C'MON!

138

139

148

THIS ISN'T FUNNY!!!

164

YEP... STILL HEALTHY AS A HORSE.

NO PARASITES, NO BACTERIA, NO FOOD ALLERGIES . . .

UM, GOOD?

SO YOUR OFFICIAL DIAGNOSIS IS **IBS.**

THAT STANDS FOR **IRRITABLE BOWEL SYNDROME.**

IT BASICALLY MEANS UPSET STOMACH . . . WITH NO DISCERNABLE CAUSE.

TAKAHASHI

CAN IT BE CURED?

IT TENDS TO COME AND GO.

GET ENOUGH REST, EXERCISE, WATER . . .

AND HOW TO FOCUS ON THEIR FEET.

AMAZINGLY, I GOT THROUGH MY PRESENTATION WITHOUT A HINT OF FEAR.

CLAP CLAP CLAP CLAP CLAP CLAP CLAP CLAP CLAP

AND **EVERYONE** SEEMED A LITTLE CALMER AFTERWARD.

RINNNNNG

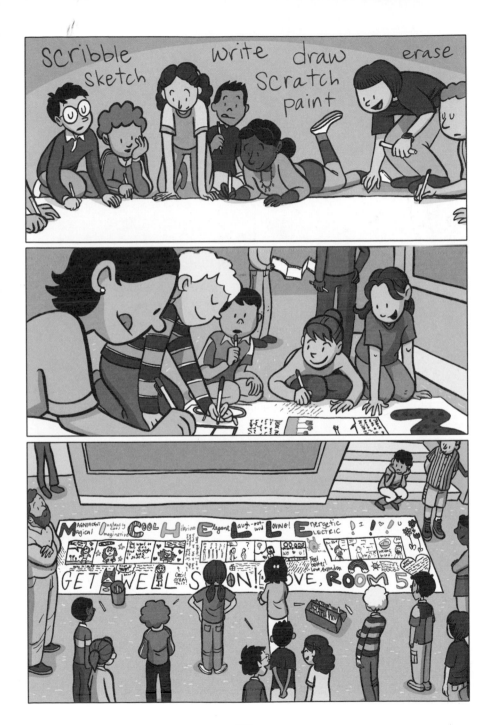

Thanks to . . .

Early readers: Andy Runton, Vera Brosgol, Casey Gilly, Mike Jung, Shannon Hale, and Sue Telgemeier.

Consultants: Dr. Judy Pelham and Dr. Frank F. Escobar-Roger.

Production assistant: Meggie Ramm.

The team at Scholastic: Cassandra Pelham Fulton, David Saylor, Phil Falco, Lauren Donovan, Ellie Berger, Tracy van Straaten, Lizette Serrano, Julie Amitie, Carmen Alvarez, Susan Lee, Holland Baker, Celia Lee, Akshaya Iyer, and Shivana Sookdeo.

Colorists: Braden Lamb and Shelli Paroline.

My agent, Judy Hansen.

My family!

My therapists!!

My lovely and comforting group of friends, for whom no topic is off-limits.

My readers, who always ask the best questions.

— Raina

Author's Note

Guts was inspired by real people, real therapy, and real memories from my fourth- and fifth-grade years, though I adjusted some minor details to make the reading experience more streamlined.

I've dealt with stomachaches and anxiety for most of my life. It has never been easy, but it's gotten better as I've learned how to manage it over the years. My panic attacks came out of nowhere, starting at age nine. I missed a lot of school. I became obsessed with every little funny feeling in my stomach. I was terrified of eating the "wrong" foods, convinced they would make me ill. (The clinical term for fear of vomit is *emetophobia*, and it's actually pretty common!)

So, how am I doing now, more than three decades after this story takes place?

In the past five years I have done talk therapy, cognitive behavioral therapy, mindfulness training, EMDR, and exposure therapy. I tried anxiety medication. I use meditation apps. They've all helped, but I've realized that my phobias and worries are just part of who I am. I do my best to manage them!

I've been tested for everything from celiac disease to Crohn's disease to ulcerative colitis, and, after many negative results, I've learned to accept that there's nothing medically "wrong" with my stomach. I just have a sensitive system and must be careful about what I eat. My anxiety also affects how my body feels! So when I'm stressed out, I'm more likely to have digestion issues.

I want to make sure my readers know that this is my personal story. You may recognize some of my struggles, or yours might be totally different. You might not experience physical or emotional stress at all. If you do find yourself feeling stressed, or you're hurting in a way that you don't understand, please talk to an adult you know and trust. I was very lucky to have people in my life who supported me and helped me find ways to feel better.

Finally, I want to encourage you to talk about how you feel. You can write it down, draw pictures or comics, make music or plays, or simply share with your friends. It takes guts to admit how you feel on the inside, but chances are, others will be able to relate. You won't know unless you try!

Also by
Raina Telgemeier

Smile

Sisters

DRAMA

By Ann M. Martin
and Raina Telgemeier

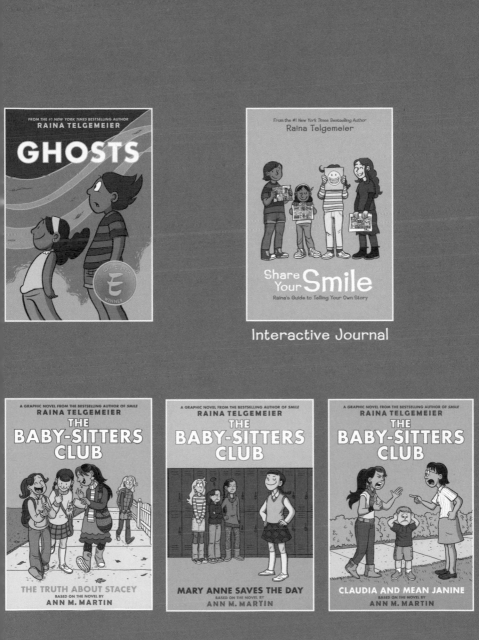

GHOSTS

FROM THE #1 NEW YORK TIMES BESTSELLING AUTHOR
RAINA TELGEMEIER

From the #1 New York Times Bestselling Author
Raina Telgemeier

Share Your Smile
Raina's Guide to Telling Your Own Story

Interactive Journal

A GRAPHIC NOVEL FROM THE BESTSELLING AUTHOR OF SMILE
RAINA TELGEMEIER
THE BABY-SITTERS CLUB
THE TRUTH ABOUT STACEY
BASED ON THE NOVEL BY
ANN M. MARTIN

A GRAPHIC NOVEL FROM THE BESTSELLING AUTHOR OF SMILE
RAINA TELGEMEIER
THE BABY-SITTERS CLUB
MARY ANNE SAVES THE DAY
BASED ON THE NOVEL BY
ANN M. MARTIN

A GRAPHIC NOVEL FROM THE BESTSELLING AUTHOR OF SMILE
RAINA TELGEMEIER
THE BABY-SITTERS CLUB
CLAUDIA AND MEAN JANINE
BASED ON THE NOVEL BY
ANN M. MARTIN

Raina Telgemeier is the #1 *New York Times* bestselling, multiple Eisner Award-winning creator of *Smile* and *Sisters*, which are both graphic memoirs based on her childhood. She is also the creator of *Drama* and *Ghosts*, and is the adapter and illustrator of the first four Baby-sitters Club graphic novels. Raina lives in the San Francisco Bay Area. To learn more, visit her online at goRaina.com.